Dinosaur

THE DINOSAUR NATIONAL MONUMENT QUARRY

BY LINDA WEST AND DAN CHURE
ADDITIONAL MATERIAL BY GREER CHESHER

ILLUSTRATIONS BY LINDA WEST
AND CLINT MCKNIGHT

PUBLISHED BY THE
DINOSAUR NATURE ASSOCIATION
1291 EAST HIGHWAY 40
VERNAL, UTAH 84078-2830
www.dinosaurnature.com

A Dinosaur Hunter's Dream

How did *you* first meet dinosaurs? In books? A visit to a museum? Watching *The Flintstones?* Earl Douglass' introduction was a little more dramatic—he discovered the world's greatest single deposit of Jurassic fossil dinosaur bones, which later became the focal point of Dinosaur National Monument.

Douglass didn't stumble on this buried treasure by accident. He was actually looking for dinosaur bones. But why? And why in this particular place? Douglass was a paleontologist (a scientist studying prehistoric life from its fossil remains) employed by the Carnegie Museum of Pittsburgh, Pennsylvania. His original specialty was fossil mammals, and the search for them had brought him to the Uinta Basin of northeastern Utah in 1907. In 1908 Dr. W. J. Holland, the Museum director, came out to see how Douglass was doing, and suggested that they make a reconnaissance of some older rocks on the northern edge of the basin—rocks that had yielded dinosaur fossils in other areas.

No wonder Earl Douglass was smiling—he had discovered one of the richest dinosaur fossil deposits in the world. When this photograph was taken, about 1922, the Carnegie Museum (Douglass' employer) had already quarried plenty of bones for its own exhibits, so Douglass was supervising excavations for the Smithsonian Institution. The thigh bone under his hand is now part of a complete *Diplodocus* standing in the Smithsonian.

Holland, perhaps, was hoping to fulfill the wish of the Museum's benefactor, Andrew Carnegie. The steel tycoon, so the story goes, was viewing the huge new exhibit hall that his millions had helped to build, and said, "Fill that room with something *big."* So, looking for something big, Douglass and Holland explored the rugged terrain along the Green River north of the small town of Jensen. They found something big—a dinosaur thigh bone six feet long. It was too big for them to carry out on foot or horseback, but it and other fragmentary fossils convinced them that Douglass should renew the search the following year.

The rocks that lured Douglass into tramping up and down hot, barren ridges and gullies for another season are a group of sedimentary layers that occur over a wide area, from the Black Hills and northern plains to the Colorado Plateau of the Southwest. The strata are typically greenish-gray with eye-catching bands of red, purple, and other colors, but something else in them had caught the eye of a Colorado schoolmaster in 1877. Exploring the hills west of Denver, he recognized the bones of "some gigantic saurian" in the rocks. Within months, other enormous fossils were discovered in similar rocks near Cañon City, Colorado, and Como Bluff, Wyoming. These finds triggered a "dinosaur rush" which, though it was limited to a few scientists and their teams of collectors, was no less intense than the gold and silver rushes of the same era. The rainbow-hued strata became known as the Morrison Formation, after a little town near the site of the first discovery.

The Morrison Formation originated on low-lying river floodplains about 150 million years ago. That was close to the middle of the dinosaurs' long reign as the world's dominant land animals, or, in geologists' terms, in the last part of the Jurassic Period. Dinosaurs continued to flourish for the next 70 or 80 million years—the Cretaceous Period—but not in the area that is now Dinosaur National Monument. During this period, long fin-

The bones that gave away the location of the fossil deposit were these weathered-out vertebrae of the large dinosaur *Apatosaurus*. George Goodrich, a local man who was helping Douglass in his search for fossils, posed by the bones with a shovel that would soon be put to long, hard use.

gers of the sea crept inland and flooded most of the center of North America, including the Colorado Plateau region. Layer after layer of mud, silt, and sand settled on the floors and beaches of this waterway, burying the Morrison Formation and its pockets of dinosaur bones under thousands of feet of sediments.

Already preserved from decay by fairly rapid burial in river sands and gravels which hardened into a tough sandstone, the bones that Douglass would later discover were now well-protected by this mile-thick covering. They were also, of course, very well hidden. However, sometime near the end of the Cretaceous Period, the restlessness of the Earth's crust began to change that situation, as North America shrugged off the last inland sea and a period of mountain-building began. The once-level sedimentary layers were squeezed and cracked and buckled upward to form the Rocky Mountains. (You could visualize this process by taking this book, with its pages representing the neatly-layered strata, and crumpling it up, though

Straining on the ropes, three early quarry workers show the back-breaking effort required to hoist an *Apatosaurus* thigh bone from its stony bed. Filled with hard minerals, still partly encased in heavy rock, and wrapped in burlap and plaster to protect them during shipment to the Carnegie Museum, some of the largest specimens weighed as much as five tons.

this is not recommended if you wish to read further.) Along with the injection of molten rock from below, this mountain-building probably destroyed any buried bones that might have been in the area of the Rockies.

To the west, though, things were a little quieter. The region that is now roughly centered on the Four Corners, where Utah, Colorado, New Mexico, and Arizona meet, rose up with the mountains but remained fairly level, forming the great upland of the Colorado Plateau. Here and there the strata were compressed enough to warp upward or downward—again using this book as an example, you can squeeze gently on the sides until the pages form a broad arch. The greatest such bending occurred along the northern edge of the Plateau, where the layers sag deeply downward to form the Uinta Basin, then swell up in a huge rock wave—called the Uinta Mountains—that curls across the top of Utah. If all the strata that had been deposited through the end of the Cretaceous Period were still present, the Uintas would be higher than the Himalayas.

However, the old saying, "What goes up must come down," applies as much to geological processes as to anything else. The higher the rocks rose, the more vigorously they were attacked by rain, snow, ice, wind, and the constant tug of gravity. Grain by grain, then layer by layer, the tops of the mountains crumbled and began working their way downhill, carried along by rockfalls, avalanches, streams, and rivers. Eventually, the sedimentary strata—including the long—buried Morrison Formation—were totally stripped from the top of the range, with only their eroded edges showing in tilted rows along the flanks. This did not all happen overnight. The mountain-building probably took place a little at a time over several million years; the erosion began at the same time and is still going on. Had someone been around with a time-lapse camera set to take one frame per year, the resulting movie would take a full month to show at normal speed, and Earl Douglass would enter the scene about three seconds before the end. Let's stop the projector and take a closer look at the 1909 frame.

Carnegie Museum workers back in Pittsburgh faced equally hard work in uncrating, cleaning, and assembling the bones. Supported by a maze of scaffolding, wires, and chains, the huge skeleton of *Apatosaurus* slowly began to take shape *(left)*. Many of the steel supports *(right)* were cast from special molds to make an exact fit with the vertebrae.

Douglass returned to Utah from Pittsburgh in the spring of that year and spent a month or two exploring various sites, but found nothing more than fragmentary dinosaur remains. In August he focused his attention on an area just across the Green River from where he and Holland had found the big thigh bone the previous year. Here, the Uinta Mountains taper off into a series of smaller folds, one of them called Split Mountain because the Green River has cut a deep gorge directly through it. The Morrison Formation and other strata encircle the foot of Split Mountain in a series of narrow ridges and valleys.

On August 17th, Douglass scrambled up one such ridge, formed by a thin, hard sandstone layer that had resisted erosion longer than the softer rocks on either side. Other human feet might have walked there before his, but it's likely that no human eyes ever noticed what his did: eight large vertebrae half-embedded in the rock. They were a little weatherbeaten, but were still neatly attached together just as they had been when they formed part of the tail of a long-extinct *Brontosaurus*. The thigh bone he had found earlier had been bigger, but it was only one bone. These held more promise—the possibility that more of the skeleton lay beneath them in the steeply-tilted sandstone. Douglass was not exaggerating when he opened his diary that night and wrote, "It was a beautiful sight."

The sight became even more beautiful as Douglass carefully chipped into the rock, following the line of the tail, and found that the bones continued. Within a few days, he was able to estimate that the whole animal had been about 60 feet long, and to predict that this would be one of the best *Brontosaurus* (more properly *Apatosaurus,* as explained on page 46,)

Six years after Earl Douglass first saw it, the *Apatosaurus* stood completed in the Carnegie Museum's exhibit hall— except for Its head, that is. Due to a long debate over which skull belonged to it, the skeleton did not begin wearing its present head until 1979.

specimens ever found. The latter proved to be correct. The skeleton—although some sections were folded back on each other, scattered, or missing—was and still is the most nearly complete *Apatosaurus* known. However, Douglass had to revise his guess at its size when he followed the tail in the other direction and found that it kept going, tapering down to a long "whiplash" previously unknown in *Apatosaurus*. Six years later—the time it took to excavate,

the spring of 1911 he decided to work westward along the quarry ridge. It was a good choice; immediately more bones and skeletons began to turn up, sometimes literally piled one on top of another. Sauropods—the big long-necked, long-tailed herbivores such as *Apatosaurus* and its kin—continued to predominate, but scattered *Stegosaurus* remains were abundant enough to cause Douglass to grumble that they were often in the way of the

ship, restore, and assemble it in the Carnegie Museum's Dinosaur Hall—the mounted skeleton stood almost 15 feet tall at the hips, and stretched over 70 feet in length. As Carnegie wished, Douglass had found something big.

But this is getting ahead of the story. Even in the first weeks of work, during which Douglass hired several local men to help in the excavation, the quarry began to hint that it would be special in more ways than one. Mixed with the first skeleton were parts of three more apatosaurs, one of them a very small juvenile; a partial *Stegosaurus*, the bizarre plate-backed dinosaur; and dozens of scattered bones from these and other types of dinosaurs. These kept Douglass and his helpers busy for the next year and a half.

Douglass recognized the deposit as the work of an ancient river that had collected and buried numerous dinosaur bodies in varying states of decay, and from the way the bones lay he deduced that the current had flowed from west-to-east. In

prized sauropods. Carnivorous dinosaurs proved to be rare, but a reasonably good skeleton and skull of *Allosaurus,* the largest predator of its time, had been unearthed by 1914. And still there were more bones.

Ultimately it took nearly seven years to excavate the western half of the quarry. If that seems like a long time to spend digging up old bones, remember that this was no ordinary digging. The sandstone in which almost all the bones lay was only about 10 to 15 feet thick, but it plunged underground at a steep angle and was covered by a much greater thickness of clay layers—all of which had to be "mucked out" with picks and shovels (and occasionally even small charges of dynamite) and put somewhere else. Since the quarry site was on top of a ridge cut by deep ravines at either end, it was convenient to dump this overburden down the ravines. Eventually the crew acquired a small hand-pushed mining car to speed up the hauling and dumping of the waste rock, but they still had to pull up and re-lay its tracks with each deepening of the cut along the bone layer.

And that was just the preliminary work. the sandstone itself was often as hard as granite, but dynamite could not safely be used in it because of the danger of blowing the bones to bits. The men had to work their way into the sandstone by drilling vertical holes at about one-foot intervals, then pounding wedges into the holes until the rock cracked. Drilling, as described by one of the workers, was a rough, dangerous job that usually required two men:

over 50 miles of dusty roads to the mining camp of Dragon, Utah. From there the narrow-gauge Uintah Railway took them on to the transcontinental lines at Mack, Colorado. Over the years, nine boxcar loads of bones made the long trip east.

Once the fossils reached the Carnegie Museum, the enormous task of unpacking, cleaning, and sorting them began. Had it not been for the careful records that Douglass kept, the latter job would have

The quarry workers gradually cut a deep trench alongside the bone-bearing sandstone (the rock on the left). Horsedrawn scrapers helped to clear away some surface rubble, but most of the digging was pick-and-shovel work. Waste rock was loaded into the small mining car and dumped into a ravine below.

...one man striking with a "double jack," a sledge hammer, as the second man rotated the drill... The man with the drill would be sitting on the ground with his knees akimbo, holding the drill between his knees. He had learned early to make no extraneous movement until the man with the sledge hammer had stopped his striking operation. Otherwise, grave consequences could result.

This large-scale stonecutting stopped, of course, whenever a fossil was encountered. Smaller chisels were used to chip away the rock close to the bone, which was then covered with tissue paper followed by burlap strips dipped in plaster. When the plaster hardened, the resulting jacket protected the bone as chiseling continued around and behind it, until the whole block of bone and rock could be pried loose. More of the sandstone was then chipped off, and the rest of the block was plastered, packed in straw, and enclosed in a sturdy wooden crate for its journey to Pittsburgh.

From the quarry, horse-drawn freight wagons hauled the crated fossils south

been like taking inventory in a china shop whose last customer had been a bull. Every bone, large or small, was given a number, and each whole or partial skeleton received a separate number to distinguish it from other skeletons. Further, to record the original relationships of the bones as they had lain in the rock, Douglass had a huge grid of four-foot squares painted directly on the quarry face, and as each bone was uncovered, he sketched it and noted its number on a chart with a similar grid. Once in a while mixups did occur. For instance, one skeleton that had been nearly complete when

After breaking the fossil bones free from the rock, the workers wrapped them in thick "jackets" of burlap strips dipped in plaster, then crated them for shipment. The dark lines on the rock were part of the grid system that Douglass used to keep track of the bones' original locations. Sightseers were frequent even in the early days, so a sign by the ladder admonished: "Please do not molest bones."

Ups and Downs of a Dinosaur Hill.

1. About 150 million years ago, a winding river buried thousands of dinosaur bones in the sand and gravel of its channel. The sandbar that would eventually become the site of the quarry is shown as a dark-brown sliver in this and the following cross-sections.

2. More river floodplain deposits (gray), then the sands and muds of inland seas (yellow), covered the sandbar to a depth of several thousand feet. The weight of these sediments began to compress and solidify the buried sandbar. The seepage of mineral-laden waters further cemented it into hard sandstone and fossilized the bones within it.

3. Compression of the Earth's crust buckled the strata upward into an arch shape, steeply tilting the sandbar and the layers around it. The sandbar area, outlined in black, is enlarged to show more detail in the remaining diagrams.

4. Even as the uplift and tilting happened, erosion began to wear away the top and sides of the arch. The buried sandbar stayed in the same place, but the ground surface gradually eroded lower and lower, drawing closer to it.

5. By 1909, some of the sandbar itself had been exposed and partly worn away. Eight dinosaur tail bones were showing near the top of the ridge formed by the hard sandstone, and Earl Douglass saw them.

6. After 15 years of quarrying, Douglass and his workers had sliced deep into the top of the ridge, and had totally stripped the bone-bearing sandstone from an area (shown in white) longer than a football field. They had cut further downward at the ends of the ridge than in the center. That center area would lie untouched for the next 30 years.

7. From 1933 to 1938, a WPA crew widened and slightly deepened the cut in the ridge top, but left a 10-foot thickness of clay layers (gray) to cover and protect the remaining center part of the bone deposit.

8. When the National Park Service reopened the quarry in the 1950s, the workers first stripped off the soft clay strata to expose the bone layer, then began to uncover a few bones. The tin shed provided a winter work area and sheltered the first part of the new exhibit: several bones left in place in the sandstone face.

9. The bone-bearing sandstone forms one wall of the present Quarry Visitor Center. Inside, visitors gaze at more than 1,600 dinosaur bones still lying where the ancient river buried them, The bone layer may extend some distance further underground, but there are no plans to excavate there—and risk undermining the building—in the near future.

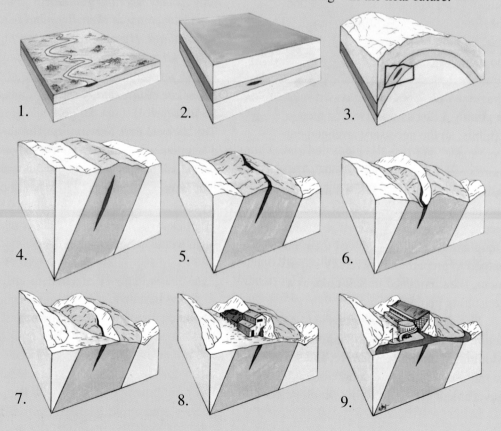

1. 2. 3.

4. 5. 6.

7. 8. 9.

A view of the Quarry Visitor Center shows the steep tilt of the rock layers around it. Only one of those layers—a hard sandstone about 10 to 15 feet thick—contains dinosaur fossils. This is the layer which forms the building's main wall.

Under the direction of the National Park Service, quarrying began again in the 1950s. The bones exposed outside lay in soft, crumbly strata, and were removed for protection from the weather. Inside the tin shed, though, the workers began to expose a few bones in the harder sandstone, and left them embedded in the rock—the beginning of the unique in-place exhibit.

Visitors on the observation deck inside the quarry building have a dinosaur's-eye view of the sand-stone face embedded with some 1,600 fossil bones.

Uncovering the Wall of Bones

Although The Great Depression stunted park finances, the Works Progress Administration at least provided some manpower. From 1933 to 1938, the WPA employed a crew of 50 to 100 men who initiated the second phase of the quarry's development. These workers didn't actually excavate any fossils, but they widened and deepened the cut made by Douglass' earlier quarrying. They left the bone layer itself concealed and protected by a 10-foot thickness of the softer overlying sediments; a wise move, as it turned out, for when they were finished, the quarry had to wait another 15 years for the next—and ultimate—development to begin.

Just as the Smithsonian Institution had once contributed to the establishment of Dinosaur National Monument in 1953 it contributed to the re-opening of the quarry in the person of Dr. Theodore E. White. "Doc" White left a job at that museum to become the monument paleontologist—or, as he liked to put it, "chief ramrod of the chisels and hammers." His task was to

This is how the preparators spent most of their time during the reliefing of the quarry wall—not with drills, sledge hammers, or even large chisels, but with ice picks—painstakingly scrapping and prying the rock away, grain by grain, from each fossil bone.

out" that Douglass and his team had to do, except that airpowered jackhammers were now available. To help in the work, Doc White recruited two local men who were familiar with such tools and were already members of the monument's maintenance staff—Tobe Wilkins and Frank MacKnight.

The three of them set to work and spent the next four summers shaving off the outer layers. During the cold and snowy winter months, they retreated to a corrugated tin shed constructed over part of the emerging quarry face. There Wilkins and MacKnight began to learn the finer aspects of paleontology by cleaning the occasional fossils that had been removed from the soft, outer strata, and exposing a few more in the sandstone itself. Protected by the tin roof, the latter

The outer layer of sandstone here is relatively barren of fossils, so preparators were able to use heavy drills, wedges and sledge hammers to split off large chunks of rock without much danger of damaging a bone.

direct a new kind of quarrying: uncovering the fossils, but leaving them in place in the rock to form a permanent exhibit.

The first step was to reveal the bone-bearing sandstone itself by removing the last of the clay layers that still covered it. This was about the same as the "mucking

As each bone (in this instance a *Stegosaurus* back plate) was uncovered, preparators coated it with a clear preservative. This lacquer-like sealant keeps the bones from absoarbing moisture which could freeze and crack them during the cold winters.

13

Perched on a platform suspended high on the quarry face, Tobe Wilkins spent many weeks working on this *Camarasaurus* skull. His careful efforts were rewarded with the discovery of several small, delicate bones that had never before been seen in their proper positions.

Huge leg and shoulder bones of sauropods such as *Apatosaurus* and *Diplodocus* dominate many parts of the quarry face, and dwarfed the preparators working on them. Even these massive fossils were carefully exposed with small chisels and ice picks.

This jumble of *Camarasaurus* bones is actually the most nearly complete skeleton on the quarry face—though at first glance it wouldn't seem to be. At the time of its burial by sediments, the body was probably partially decayed and beginning to fall apart. Further decay, scavengers, and river currents probably all helped to mix up the bones, which were then covered with sand and gravel before they were completely scattered. The numbers on the major bones match those in the diagram to show how they would fit together in a more recognizable shape.

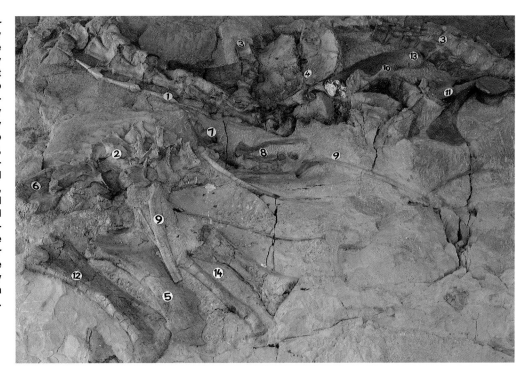

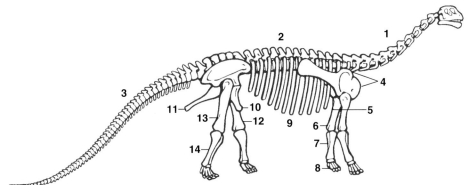

1. Neck Vertebrae
2. Back Vertebrae
3. Tail Vertebrae
4. Right Shoulder Blade
5. Left Shoulder Blade
6. Left Upper Foreleg
7. Left Lower Foreleg
8. Left Forefoot
9. Several Ribs
10. Front Hip Bones
11. Rear Hip Bones
12. Left Thigh
13. Right Thigh
14. Right Lower Hind Leg

bones were left in place, standing out in high relief from the surrounding rock to provide the first exhibit for visitors of that time.

In those days, Doc White's helpers worked on a subject-to-furlough basis, with a one-month layoff each year. During one of these furloughs, White borrowed another monument maintenance man, Jim Adams, to help at the quarry. Adams found the work interesting but had to return to road-and-trail duties when the month was up. The next time he saw the quarry, four years later, things had changed. The old tin shed was gone and in its place, enclosing the entire remaining section of the bone layer, was the nearly-completed new Quarry Visitor Center. Moreover, Frank MacKnight had decided to go back to maintenance work, and Jim Adams took his place as a fossil preparator along with Tobe Wilkins. For the next quarter-century and more, millions of visitors would literally look over Adams' and Wilkins' shoulders to witness the painstak-

ing process of dinosaur discovery.

When the present quarry building was opened in June of 1958, its first visitors walked up the sloping concrete ramp to an observation deck overlooking a wall of rock with only a few fossil bones exposed in it. By the time Adams and Wilkins retired in the early 1980s, they had uncovered some 1,600 bones. That number increased over the next few years as fossil preparators Ann Schaffer and Scott Madsen continued to scratch, chip, and drill away the hard sandstone.

Most of the task of exposing the fossils in high relief (or just "reliefing," in quarry jargon) was done with small hand tools, from hammers and chisels to ice picks—those once-common household weapons that are almost forgotten in this day of self-defrosting refrigerators. Ground down to a flat, angled tip, the ice pick could scrape rock particles off smooth bone surfaces. Sharpened to a fine point, it could pry and chip the rock from rougher bone ends, cracks, and crevices.

In ordinary fossil preparation, this grain-by-grain cleaning takes place in a laboratory, and is sometimes aided by small power tools. In Dinosaur National Monument's quarry where most of the bones were left in place, the work required countless ice picks, steady hands, and hours of patience. Such painstakingly slow work was the only way to reveal the fossils without breaking them.

*t*he quarry's "bone layer" was actually three distinct layers, separated by relatively barren rock. The first or outermost layer was not in the sandstone itself, but in the softer overlying clay that was removed in the 1950s. Fossils in this layer were scarce, as they also were in the second layer, the outer part of the sandstone. This second layer was mostly removed, except for a large slab containing a jumbled sauropod skeleton near the west end of the building, and a low ledge which runs along the bottom of the quarry face. The third layer, the rear part of the sandstone, contains the best-preserved and most abundant fossil bones. It is this layer which has been left intact, with as many bones as possible exposed within it.

During the most active era of quarry work, the visitor center rang with the clamor of power drills and sledgehammers pounded upon steel wedges. These tools can still be seen, now resting like the bones themselves, where they were laid down over a decade ago. Visitors today must shudder at the thought of pulverized dinosaur bones floating in the dust from the drills. Such drilling, wedging, and splitting, however, took place only in the "boneless" rock between the second and third fossil layers. The preparators kept a good supply of strong epoxy on hand for rare mishaps, as well as for patching the natural cracks that often ran through the bones.

The few fossils that were removed along with the second layer got the same treatment that Douglass gave his treasures. Even though these bones traveled only the short distance to the paleontological laboratory, they still received protective plaster-and-burlap jackets, which served to hold loose fragments together and prevent further cracking or chipping. After final cleaning in the lab, a few outstanding specimens were placed on display; the others become part of the monument's study collection. This collection, available both to the quarry paleontological staff and to visiting scientists, is a valuable resource which helps in the identification of new specimens, provides data for research, and preserves a number of rare fossils that are the best, and sometimes the only, examples of their kind.

In 1977, Jim Adams began removing these small *Stegosaurus* leg bones from the quarry face *(1)*. First uncovered years earlier, the bones had been left in place like most of the quarry's fossils, but interest in them grew with the realization that they were the smallest *Stegosaurus* bones ever found. Careful probing into the rock revealed several more bones from the same animal. To protect the exposed bone surfaces during removal, Jim covered them with burlap-and-plaster jackets *(2)*. Then, chiseling into the rock behind them, he pried them off the quarry face and took them into the laboratory *(3)*, where he spent many months cleaning the rock off them and peeling off the plaster *(4)*. The bones proved to be too breakable to be put on display, so Jim made rubber molds from them and poured in casting resin to make exact replicas of each bone *(5)*. These were then attached to a steel framework for the finished exhibit in the quarry's museum section *(6)*.

1.

2.

3.

One such unique specimen, the world's smallest *Stegosaurus,* is a sharp contrast to the gigantic bones that dominate the quarry. Some of the leg bones of this collie-sized juvenile had been uncovered soon after the visitor center opened, but, lying in the third layer, they were left in place. When Russell King, Doc White's successor, decided in 1977 that they were worth a more detailed look, Jim Adams began the delicate task of removing them from the quarry face and searching for more of the skeleton, if it existed. Eventually he uncovered more of the limbs, a shoulder blade, a good part of the hips, and several ribs—hardly a complete skeleton, but certainly more extensive than any other known juvenile *Stegosaurus.* The actual fossils are too fragile for display (the ribs, for instance, are pencil-thin), but King felt that durable resin-and-fiberglass casts of them would make an interesting new exhibit. Tragically, he drowned in a fishing accident and never saw the results. When paleontologist Dan Chure arrived on the scene in 1979, he was just in time to help Tobe Wilkins wrestle a steel rod into a framework to support the cast replica of "Baby Stego," which made its debut in the quarry exhibits the following spring.

Today, visitors no longer see workers patiently working to expose bones on the great wall. In 1991, with the building's fossil-bearing vein about "played out", the focus of the monument's paleontological efforts moved to several promising new locations beyond the visitor center. These new quarries are yielding spectacular information about the ecosystem the dinosaurs lived in, marking an exciting new chapter in the history of the monument. hatever the future holds, there will only be

one original "Quarry" at Dinosaur National Monument. This historic site has yielded an unparalleled treasure of dinosaur fossils—from petite juveniles to colossal adults—in more detail than ever before. Moreover, the quarry today helps us see the broader picture of the Jurassic world and its amazing community of life. Nowhere else on Earth can you stand on the very spot where dinosaurs once lived and see so many of their bones still in their final resting place. Rarely do we get such a vivid look through the shuttered windows of the past.

4.

5.

6.

A Stack of Time.

Through comparison with rock layers and fossils all over the world, geologists can sketch the broad outline of Earth history and the development of life, as shown on this geologic time scale. The various eras and periods were first defined on the basis of fossils discovered in the early 1800s. Not until the 1950s did radioactive-dating methods provide estimates of the actual ages of some strata. As more such dates became available, geologists were able to incorporate them into the established time scale.

This chart portrays one representative animal for each time period. Some of these, such as the horned dinosaur, lived only during the Cretaceous Period in which it is shown; others span much longer times. Dragonflies, for instance, are still around today, though none can match the 30" wingspan of some of their Pennsylvanian Period ancestors.

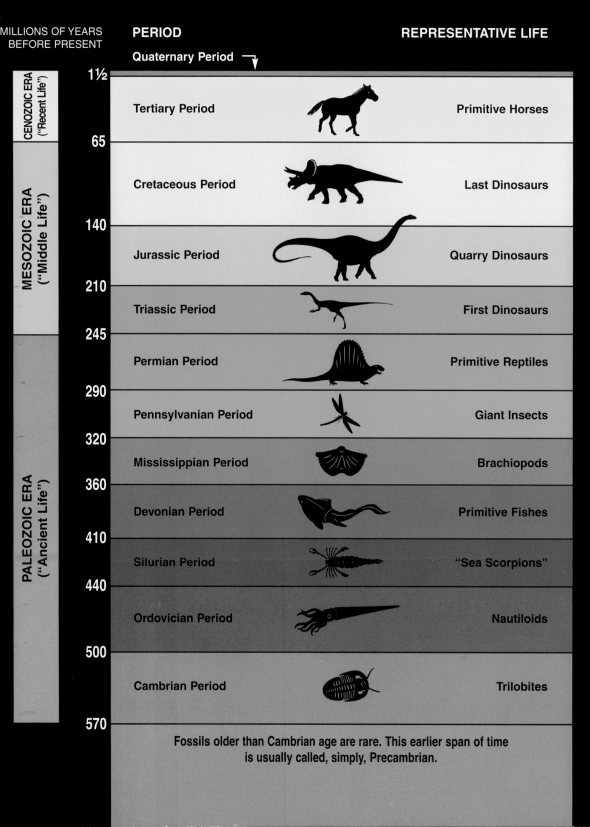

MILLIONS OF YEARS BEFORE PRESENT	PERIOD	REPRESENTATIVE LIFE
	Quaternary Period	
1½		
	Tertiary Period	Primitive Horses
65		
	Cretaceous Period	Last Dinosaurs
140		
	Jurassic Period	Quarry Dinosaurs
210		
	Triassic Period	First Dinosaurs
245		
	Permian Period	Primitive Reptiles
290		
	Pennsylvanian Period	Giant Insects
320		
	Mississippian Period	Brachiopods
360		
	Devonian Period	Primitive Fishes
410		
	Silurian Period	"Sea Scorpions"
440		
	Ordovician Period	Nautiloids
500		
	Cambrian Period	Trilobites
570		

CENOZOIC ERA ("Recent Life")

MESOZOIC ERA ("Middle Life")

PALEOZOIC ERA ("Ancient Life")

Fossils older than Cambrian age are rare. This earlier span of time is usually called, simply, Precambrian.

A World of Questions

The Morrison Ecosystem Project transformed our understanding of the Jurassic environment from a dry, unyielding desert into a vibrant, dynamic ecosystem resembling Africa's Serengeti Plain.

oday, the most famous dinosaur quarry on earth has been unworked in any significant way for over 50 years. The ring of hammer and chisel is gone; the amazing display of bones standing in quiet dignity.

Quiet, that is, until Dinosaur National Monument Paleontologist Dan Chure assembled the Morrison Ecosystem Project, a multi-disciplinary, multi-institutional, international team bent on reviving Dinosaur's ancient environment. For the first time, the focus of paleontological research here has shifted from the quarry to the miles of unexplored Morrison Formation flowing through the Monument. The project's results have transformed the Morrison from a dry, unyielding desert into a vibrant, dynamic ecosystem resembling Tanzania's busy Serengeti Plain.

In the past, contradictory data prevented scientists from creating an integrated concept of the living Morrison. "One problem," Chure says, "is that we had no hard dates for the Morrison. Previous estimates for its deposition range from 5 to 20 million years! Without more precise dates, there's no way to know if dinosaurs from different Morrison quarries lived at the same time. A second problem is that

dinosaur skeletons tell us little about the environment. We don't know what the Morrison climate and ecosystem were like, so we have no real idea what herbivorous dinosaurs were eating. And finally, we don't know what the Morrison environment looked like as a whole."

To answer these questions and resolve ongoing controversies, Chure explains, "we completed a paleoinventory of the Morrison—not only of the Formation's dinosaurs, but also its microfossils, invertebrates, small vertebrates, fossil soils, ichnofossils (trace fossils), and even pollen. Then we studied the Morrison's stratigraphy and depositional environments to develop a geologic framework for the paleoinventory and provide a way to relate distant quarries." Chure calls the volumes of data gathered "a feast of information." Each finding, interesting in itself, took on greater significance when placed in the developing narrative of the new Morrison.

For example, in Virginia, Ron Litwin, a palynologist with the U.S. Geological Survey extracted pollen and spores from the Morrison. The study of pollen, called palynology, can address a formation's general climate and relative age. "A relative date," Litwin explains, "is 'the time of the Civil War'; an absolute date is 1864. By radiometrically dating volcanic ash found sporadically in the Morrison, Bart Kowallis (of BYU) established a number of absolute dates." In layers without ash, pollen can establish relative ages across hundreds of miles.

As vegetation changed through geologic time," Litwin continues, "certain associations of pollen became characteristic of a certain period. In the past, scientists who looked at the Morrison using only stratigraphic relationships concluded that some of it was probably deposited during the Cretaceous. But, using radiometric and relative dating our study determined that the Morrison was most likely deposited solely within the late Jurassic and over a fairly short time."

Dan Chure adds, "These studies indicate, for the first time, that the Morrison was deposited between 155 and 147 million years ago—in eight million years. And this finally gives us a fairly robust idea of the sequence of the major Morrison quarries relative to one another."

In pollen, scientists also see traces of the Morrison climate. During his study, Litwin found over 225 diverse pollens and spores, most from lower vascular plants like ferns, indicating the Morrison was much more vegetated than previously thought. "There's been an ongoing scientific discussion," Litwin explains, "about whether dinosaurs existed during Morrison times in a fairly arid or a fairly humid environment." Previous pollen studies left the impression that the Morrison flora was relatively meager, suggesting an environment where tall conifers, a few cycads, and rare ferns sprouted haphazard-

ly along occasional watercourses, blowing sand dunes huddled between dry riverbeds, and sauropods extended their long necks to browse the bristly conifer tops.

Litwin acknowledges that dinosaur physiology might have been very different from that of animals today, "but," he says, "given sauropod size it seems they would use a fair bit of food to function day-to-day. These giants would have to process an awful amount of food to get a decent meal from pine needles, and I'm not certain they would get the nutrition they required. Further, conifers don't regenerate quickly."

Litwin's studies indicate there were indeed tall conifers, but beneath them grew a vibrant understory of dozens of ginkgo species, extensive cycad-like plants, abundant horsetail species, an astounding variety of ferns, rampant rushes, and copious clubmosses, i.e., a medley of potential meals.

"These types of plants prefer a moister habitat," Litwin concludes. "What we've found from examining pollen sites throughout the Morrison is reasonable evidence for a fairly equitable climate that had a fair bit of moisture periodically. But remember it's a function of time and scale. I don't think it's fully accurate to say that the Morrison was wet or that it was dry. Many, many intervals could fit within the Morrison's eight-million-year time frame."

To get a better handle on the climate, Christine Turner and Fred Peterson, both of the U.S. Geological Survey in Colorado, studied the Morrison's sediments. "When we look at the sedimentology," Fred Peterson says, "we find three main lines of evidence: gypsum at the Morrison's base, blowing sand deposits up through the formation's middle, and, above that, deposits left by carbonate and saline-alkaline lakes—all indicators of aridity."

"The lake stories really give us insight into the climate," Turner adds, "carbonate lakes and saline-alkaline deposits indicate there wasn't much surface water coming into these lakes. High mineral concentrations show that evapotranspiration was extremely high, which tells you that it was warm and dry enough of the time to really crank up the rate of evaporation." In fact, the alkalinity at times would have been strong enough to burn human skin. "There were intervals, however, when the lakes received significant surface runoff, and we get nice pond deposits. So there were times in the lake when it was nice and fresh, when there were lovely plants, but thereafter, the lake again experienced high alkalinity. The sedimentology," Turner concludes, "tells us that the climate was predominately semi-arid to arid."

These interpretations left unsolved the ongoing debate between plant taxonomists—who looked at ferns and cycad-like plants and reasoned that the abundance of moisture-loving flora indicated a humid environment—and sedimentologists—who examined alkaline lakes, blowing sand, and gypsum deposits and determined the Morrison was almost desert-like. A critical integration came from Judy Parrish. Turner calls Parrish's work, "a significant breakthrough. Now we're able to reconcile those two different interpretations."

In Tucson, Judy Parrish, Professor of Geosciences at the University of Arizona worked to resolve the climate controversy. Parrish studies taphonomy, the science of what happens to organisms after they die and before they're found by paleontologists. She explains, "I looked at the taphonomy of plant remains from a very large number of sites in the Morrison and I came to the conclusion that the environment was semi-arid. But when Ron Litwin found 225 pollen and spore taxa in the Morrison, things got very interesting.

This softer rock on the surface of the Morrison has weathered to the consistency of crumbly popcorn, and can be easily brushed away to reveal the harder, bone-bearing rock beneath it.

"The fact that we found relatively few leaf fossils—about 35 species—tells us something about the vegetation that we wouldn't know if we had just the pollen or just the leaves. In general," Parrish explains, "leaves of woody plants are the ones that tend to be preserved, not so much those of herbaceous plants. So, if you have a lot of different types of pollen and not anywhere near that number of leaf fossils, you probably had a very large component of herbaceous plants." "This plant composition," says Parrish, "is consistent with a semi-arid climate.

"People have a tendency to associate ferns with wet, tropical climates, but in fact ferns occur in a very wide variety of environments. Ferns need water to reproduce, but they don't need water, necessarily, to live. It's clear from the pollen evidence that the diversity of these groups was much higher than we see today. Without competition from grasses and other flowering plants, ferns, along with small cycads, were very likely the predominate ground cover."

"The analogy I use," Parrish continues, "is the savanna of Africa—immense grasslands with some shrubs and trees scattered around." In the Jurassic, we would have seen great fernlands with a tangle of conifers, various *Bennettitales* (cycad-like plants), and other plants close to the watercourses. "I think the high productivity of these systems would have been enough to support large animal herds just as you see in the Serengeti today.

Hand bones of a juvenile *Dryosaurus*, the best preserved and most complete ever discovered. This is the smallest of the dinosaur species known from the Morrison. Though adults grew to be 4 to 6 feet long and 150 pounds, they could scarcely be called "thunder lizards".

21

he colorful "rainbow beds" (inset) that characterize the Morrison Formation make interesting scenery but rarely contain significant fossils. The crumbly mudstone of these strata originated as thin layers of mud and silt on ancient river floodplains. Here a dinosaur carcass would most likely have rotted away before the sediments could cover and preserve it. Only in the main river channels, where stronger currents quickly covered them with sand and gravel, did dinosaur bones have a good chance to be preserved as fossils.

"Interestingly," Parrish adds, "a couple other things came out that are consistent with a herbaceous vegetation, like the work Kent Stevens and Mike Parrish (no relation) did on sauropod necks."

Under a sauropod skeleton just outside Dinosaur National Monument, two scientists pondered whether an 80-foot-long, 30-ton animal could bend its extensive neck into often-depicted swan-like poses. The two, Mike Parrish, Biology Department Chair at Northern Illinois University, and Kent Stevens, Professor of Computer Science at the University of Oregon, hit on the idea of modeling sauropod necks on a computer. Parrish explains, "It allows you to actually move a 23-foot neck that you can't very easily do with real specimens."

At the Carnegie Museum in Pittsburgh, Parrish and Stevens dangled from ladders above the same *Apatosaurus* and *Diplodocus* skeletons unearthed by Earl Douglass in 1909 at Dinosaur National Monument. After taking 24 painstaking measurements of each vertebrae, Parrish says, "we dumped it all into an elaborate computer program Kent developed."

When Stevens and Parrish grabbed the mouse and moved the computer-simulated sauropod necks for the first time, they were in for a jolt. "It was surprising," Parrish says, "we found that neither *Apatosaurus* or *Diplodocus* could raise their heads much above the height of their backs, meaning these sauropods were adapted to ground feeding or low browsing—not to chewing conifer tops. Rather than flexing their necks like elegant giraffes, these two sauropods must have fed like giant long-necked cows."

"As if all that wasn't enough to reinforce the idea of a Serengeti-like environment," Judy Parrish comments, "Karen Chin described plant remains found in dinosaur coprolites and discovered a pattern that's much more consistent with a herbaceous diet than a woody diet."

Chin is a National Science Foundation Post Doctorate Fellow at Stanford University who studies fossilized dinosaur dung as a way to tease out not only what dinosaurs were eating, but also the environment and climate.

Chin examined what might be a sauropod coprolite found in a Utah Morrison quarry. She says, "The quarry represented a waterhole where skeletal elements from five different herbivorous dinosaurs were recovered—*Apatosaurus, Barosaurus, Camarasaurus, Diplodocus,* and *Mymoorapleta,* an ankylosaur. Paleontologists also found rather unusual nodules that didn't look anything like the sediments.

"When I cut them open—lo and behold—they were just chock full of exquisitely preserved plant material," Chin says. "I counted 17 gymnosperm seeds, three or four fern spore packets, and distinctive stems and leaf blades that were most probably from the cycad-like *Bennettitales.* So, I determined these were probable herbivorous dinosaur coprolites.

"What's interesting," she continues, "are the implications about dinosaur diets. This dinosaur was eating lots of seeds, ferns, and cycad-like plants—high quality foods—rather than the more fibrous, bulky, and rudimental diet one might expect."

Dan Chure watches from the edge of the Carnegie Quarry parking lot; his eyes trace the Morrison's distinctive, undulating slope coursing toward Colorado. Heat ripples off the plain below while the Green River erodes ancient sediments and deposits its own.

Every year about this time it happens. Late in the day the hot, still air takes on a different cast as the western mountains release long-captive clouds. Beneath them, animals nibble at the sere foliage and await the storm. Abruptly, lightning pierces the sky and soothing water pours over the parched land. The floods come, sweeping stream banks clean and overflowing into ponds filling under monsoon skies.

Frogs wriggle from crusty burrows, their humming seesaw voices drift in the warm air. Long-dormant salamanders undulate through swelling algae, snails unfold, and clam shrimp pop from eggs laid and buried after the last storm. On shore, a rat-like mammal snatches an unlucky crayfish as turtles kerplunk in the gathering pools. Lizards scoot from rock to bush, and rattle through glassy, chattering horsetail forests.

Badlands? Not to a paleontologist. "Give me badlands or *no* lands!" says Dan Chure.

Such a scene, acted out within sight of the quarry, is both entirely different and oddly similar to those now silently enfolded in the Morrison's rainbow layers.

Ferns unroll new fronds as a herd of seven *Diplodocus* sauropods hove into view. Towering pines sway over flowing streams decked with a cacophony of shrubby tree ferns, bushy cycads, and ground-covering ferns. On a distant, unseen horizon a volcano erupts, its gray ash settling on the back of a young *Apatosaurus*. Focusing on one watercourse, dinosaurs gather, each stripping the plants within their reach. Moving on, their immense footprints fill with water, silt, and dung. In the distance the snarl of *Allosaurus;* camarasaurs cock their heads and return to nipping succulent gymnosperm leaves.

As the rains pass, prairie dog-like mammals poke their heads from communal burrows and rustle through concealing ferns. Termites scramble over 130-foot-tall nests, as dermestid beetles swarm over the rotting carcass of a stegosaur killed by a pack of young ceratosaurs.

"On television, a paleontologist walks to the top of a hill, picks up a bone, holds it at just the right camera angle against a glorious backdrop, and the entire prehistoric vista unfolds," Dan Chure says. "But into that one scene went years of work by legions of scientists. The Morrison Ecosystem Study used the newest innovative technologies to integrate many scientists' ideas and gave us the best understanding of the Morrison environment to date."

Right now, inside the Carnegie Quarry kids stare in wonder at the wall of jumbled dinosaurs, each bone imbedded in the rocky matrix of a larger story. Perhaps each hint about the now-extinct Morrison environment will help us understand our own. By the time these curious kids grow up our views of the Morrison will have progressed and changed again. "But, that's science," Dan Chure says, "answering one question only generates more." There'll be plenty of riddles left for these kids to solve. Just imagine where they'll take us."

25

The Dinosaurs of Dinosaur

*T*yrannosaurus rex! Brachiosaurus! Stegosaurus! Triceratops! These names are almost household words, and the animals they represent have fascinated children and adults, scientists and laypersons for over a century and a half. Yet not all of the well-known dinosaurs are found at the Dinosaur National Monument Quarry. Why not?

It doesn't necessarily take an expert to identify a fossil. Most people would recognize these as leg bones (thigh bones specifically), and can see that although both are about the same length, one is thicker than the other. That is one clue that distinguishes the bulky, thickboned *Apatosaurus* from its more slender cousin *Diplodocus*.

As we have said, the Morrison Formation dates from the late Jurassic Period, which geologists define as the middle part of a larger block of time known as the Mesozoic Era. Dinosaurs were the dominant land animals throughout most of that era. In fact, it is often called "The Age of Dinosaurs." Starting as small, two-legged reptiles in the Triassic Period (the first segment of the Mesozoic Era), dinosaurs evolved into a wide variety of sizes and shapes. Many became gigantic, but a few grew no larger than chickens. Some developed sharp teeth and claws for tearing flesh, while some became toothless. Some wielded horns, frills, spikes, or tail clubs for defense. Others simply relied on speed to escape their predators. These changes were occurring constantly over the whole time that dinosaurs existed, and so, not surprisingly, Jurassic dinosaurs were quite different from their Triassic predecessors, and Cretaceous dinosaurs (those that lived

A pair of ceratosaurs bring down an unwary camptosaur. Such "pack" behavior can only be hinted at in the fossil record, but the speculation is reasonable. Several modern predator species—including wolves, lions, and killer whales—are known to attack their prey in numbers.

at the close of the Mesozoic Era) were still more distinct. Not all types of dinosaurs existed at the same time, so not all of the familiar ones are found at the quarry, which preserves only a single chapter of dinosaur history.

But what a chapter it was! Although such notable creatures as *Tyrannosaurus* and *Triceratops* did not yet exist (and would not until the very end of the Cretaceous Period, some of the most spectacular animals of all-time flourished then. The late Jurassic Period was the dynasty of the giants—the sauropod dinosaurs.

*O*nce known as "brontosaurs," sauropods were apparently the most common large prehistoric wildlife of Dinosaur National Monument, as their bones constitute about three-fourths of all the quarry's dinosaur fossils. They were the largest land animals of all time. Those found at the quarry routinely grew to lengths of 70 and 80 feet, and fragmentary remains found elsewhere suggest that some may have been nearly twice that size. Their estimated weights range from a dozen to 100 tons. The average adult sauropod of the Morrison Formation weighed 20 tons—the equivalent of three or four large African elephants. Indeed, in

Some of the bones can be more difficult to identify, requiring careful study, precise measurement, and comparison with diagrams of other specimens.

If you were time-transported into the late Jurassic Period, you'd probably recognize a few animals that are still around in the modern world. Bones of crocodiles (like this small model, *left*, in a quarry exhibit) and turtles are occasionally mixed with those of their larger relatives In the quarry. No new species of dinosaurs have been found here, but this turtle *(center)*, christened *Dinochelys*, was unknown until its discovery in the quarry. This adult was about a foot long. A fist-sized juvenile *(bottom left)*, with the tiny bones of one leg preserved on its underside *(bottom right)*, has also been found in the quarry.

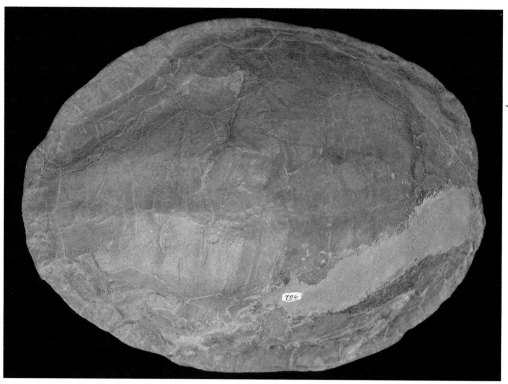

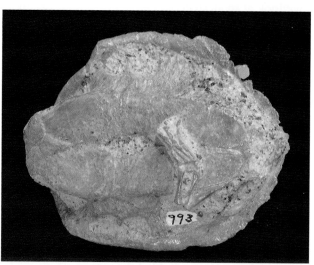

It seems fairly safe to assume that the tail spikes were defensive weapons, and that was long thought to be the function of the back plates as well. However, cross-sections through the plates reveal that they were full of cavities which may have contained blood vessels. In that case, the plates could have helped *Stegosaurus* control its body temperature by exposing large surfaces either to the sun for heating or to the wind for cooling. The number, position, and arrangement of the plates, of course, would be factors in their effectiveness for any or all of these functions. Alas, we do not know the exact number, position, and arrangement of the plates, for they were not attached directly to the vertebrae. Thus, fossil plates are rarely found close to the rest of the skeleton, and there is no conclusive evidence as to their placement on the living animal.

In addition to its puzzling plates, *Stegosaurus* had another feature that has long been the subject of a popular myth. In *Stegosaurus* and many other dinosaurs, the neural canal—the opening in the vertebrae through which the spinal cord passed—was greatly enlarged in the hip vertebrae, giving rise to the notion that an "extra brain" was housed there. In reality, what filled the space was probably no more than extra nerves which controlled the bulky muscles of the hind legs and tail. Giraffes, ostriches, and some other modern animals have such enlargements at places along their spinal cords, yet none of them are credited with having two brains. Perhaps some sympathetic observers felt that *Stegosaurus* was more in need of a little extra gray matter, as the skull space allotted to its actual brain was about the size of a walnut.

*T*hese, then were the stars of the late Jurassic show, but they were not the only players on the scene. Dinosaur National Monument, both in the quarry and at other sites, gives us glimpses of a variety of other animals that shared the Morrison Formation landscape with the dinosaurs. Though their remains are often fragmentary, many of these creatures are easier for us to understand, for unlike their more spectacular neighbors, they have living relatives that have changed very little in the last 150 million years.

Living in or near the ancient rivers—and preserved in the quarry itself—were turtles, crocodiles, and clams. The latter, in fact, are the most abundant fossils in the quarry; they are freshwater clams of the genus *Unio,* which is still common in modern rivers. The turtles, *Glyptops* and *Dinochelys,* and the crocodile, *Goniopholis,* were likewise similar in size and shape to living members of their groups.

Animals that lived and died outside of the main river channels were less likely to be fossilized, because there were fewer places on the open floodplains where sediments accumulated quickly enough to preserve their remains. However, recent surveys of other areas of the Monument where the Morrison Formation occurs have revealed a number of fossil sites that are a sharp contrast to the quarry. The rock at these sites is much finer-grained than the quarry sandstone, and probably originated in occasional quiet ponds. Such an environment was ideal for the gentle burial and preservation of many of the smaller creatures: frogs, salamanders, fish, lizards, and mammals. Many of their fossils are so small that they must be studied under a microscope.

In contrast to the Jurassic scene, today's world is dominated by the mammals. Being mammals ourselves, we humans may be inclined to take the rather superior view that our warm, furry relatives outcompeted the dinosaurs and drove them to extinction. The fossil record, enhanced by the ongoing work at Dinosaur National Monument, gives us a truer and more humbling picture. While dinosaurs existed, mammals remained small and uncommon, waiting in the wings until the stage was clear.

New Thunder
on the Horizon

On a hilltop where rocks jut up like plates on a stegosaur's back, heavy tarps weighted with boulders huff in the wind. The sun is bright, the sky deep as an ocean. Loose rock, broken from the cliff face, crackles underfoot during the steep climb up from the valley floor. Just visible in a dip between ridges, the glass-walled Dinosaur Quarry stands anchored to the Morrison Formation's multihued slope.

Here, in rocks 20 million years younger than the Morrison, burlap flaps from beneath a stone, and plaster flecks the ground. Peeling back the tarp reveals blocks leaning and sitting like freshly wrapped mummies, their gauze newly plastered over bony elbows and knees. These chalky casts do indeed encase bones; the rare bones of the first dinosaurs discovered outside the Monument's Morrison Formation.

"I can hardly overstate the significance of this find," says Dan Chure, Dinosaur National Monument paleontologist, "One block contains the complete, articulated skull and neck of a sauropod, which is almost unheard of. The fossil record for sauropod skulls is so poor that no matter where a skull is found, it's important. But this one is exceptionally important because it's so complete and because it was found in the Cedar Mountain Formation, a place where no one expected to find anything significant."

Skulls are critical to understanding evolutionary relationships between dinosaurs, and in reconstructing the environment in which they lived. However, after death, skeletons often loose their heads due to the weak articulation between skull and neck. Chure estimates that of the 200 sauropods known, a dozen at most include any adequate skull material.

New fossil finds can have far-reaching scientific effect, reorganizing well-known families or even remodeling familiar

A Colorado high school volunteer works the sauropod site with careful taps of a hammer and chisel.

skeletons. This skull might complete a recognized, but so-far headless, sauropod. Or, when compared with skull fragments lying nameless on museum shelves, it may divulge unimagined connections. Perhaps, as Chure thinks, it represents a new species from what is still an unknown world—the world of the Cedar Mountain Formation.

Sauropods dominate the older, lower Morrison Formation. In fact, in 1909 when Earl Douglass unearthed the first dinosaur at the Carnegie Quarry, it was a sauropod: brontosaurus (now called *Apatosaurus*), a 70-foot-long dinosaur 15-feet tall at the hip. Sauropods, the largest land animals of all time, grounded their massive bodies and elegantly long necks and tails on four stout legs. They grazed, sometimes in herds, through the Morrison's fern-covered hills. Then they disappeared—or so it was thought.

In the 1950s the Cedar Mountain Formation was described as "unfossiliferous." The formation had yielded little to entice paleontologists from the Morrison's bountiful quarries. However, in 1991 when the astounding *Utahraptor*—"the terror of the early Cretaceous"—clawed its way from the Cedar Mountain Formation in southeast Utah, interest, needless to say, increased. In 1998, Dinosaur National Monument preparators Scott Madsen and

The Mitten Park Fault on the Green River below Echo Park is just one example of the spectacular geology of Dinosaur National Monument.

33

The "Terrible Lizards."

These are the dinosaurs of the quarry—a complete community, from the smallest to the largest, dominated by the huge, long-necked sauropods. Similar dinosaur populations roamed China and southeastern Africa during the late Jurassic Period.

1. *Camarasaurus*—"chamber lizard," referring to hollows in its vertebrae.
2. *Barosaurus*—"heavy lizard," especially its huge, heavy neck bones.
3. *Diplodocus*—"double beam," for certain T-shaped bones in its tail.
4. *Ornitholestes*—"bird robber," supposedly quick enough to snatch a bird from the air.
5. *Apatosaurus*—"deceptive lizard," for its almost unbelievable size.
6. *Camptosaurus*—"bent lizard," referring to one of its hip bones.
7. *Allosaurus*—"other lizard," because its bones were unlike those of other dinosaurs discovered earlier.
8. *Ceratosaurus*—"horned lizard," for its distinctive and unusual horn.
9. *Dryosaurus* "oak lizard," for its oak leaf-shaped teeth.
10. *Stegosaurus*—"plated lizard," for its unique back plates.

Hunter and Hunted.

A ferocious meat-eater leaps onto the back of a huge, tail-thrashing sauropod, and clamps its deadly jaws on the hapless beast's neck. A dramatic picture? Sure. But such a scene probably did not often occur in the real Jurassic world. Like modern predators, carnivorous dinosaurs ate carrion when it was available, then only attacked animals that were relatively small and easy to kill—such as this *Camptosaurus* which is about to become lunch for *Ceratosaurus*.

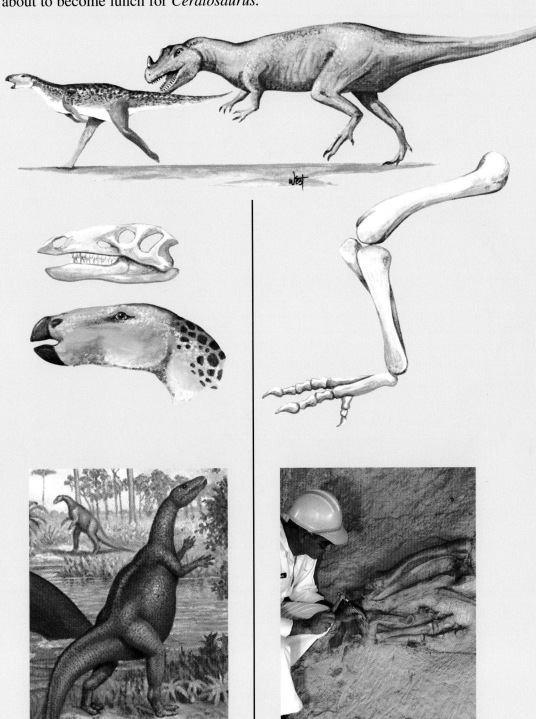

Camptosaurus had no front teeth. Instead, a horny beak for nipping off plant stems or twigs probably covered the front of its jaws. All its teeth were set far back in its mouth, and were probably enclosed by strong cheek muscles. That would have given *Camptosaurus* a rather horse-like profile, in contrast to the long lizard-like mouth depicted in this older painting.

Plant-eaters can just walk up to their food and start munching, but meat-eaters must first catch their meals. This is reflected in the slender, smooth-ended leg bones of carnivorous dinosaurs; their legs were built for flexibility and speed. The drawing here was based on leg bones of *Allosaurus,* the only carnivorous dinosaur found in more than fragmentary form in the quarry.

Rebuilding a Dinosaur From Inside Out.

A biologist can learn about a modern animal by dissecting it, working down through skin, muscles, and organs to the bones. A paleontologist must work in the opposite direction, starting with the bones. This partial restoration of *Apatosaurus* shows some of the clues a paleontologist uses to "flesh-out" the bones and envision a long-dead animal as if it were alive.

1.

2.

3.

4.

5.

1. It's not surprising that only one *Apatosaurus* skull has ever been found, for it is small and delicate compared to the massive bones of most of the body. Numerous openings in the skull helped to reduce its weight and also provided attachments and passageways for the jaw muscles. The small peglike teeth were unsuited for chewing; perhaps *Apatosaurus* used them to "rake" mouthfuls of leaves and stems from tree branches.

2. The split crests of the neck bones cradled a strong ligament that ran from the top of the neck to the middle of the back. This ligament anchored the neck and, along with smaller muscles and ligaments, raised and lowered it—much as a series of cables operate a mechanical crane.

3. Shown in side and rear views, this back vertebra resembles the vaulted arches and flying buttresses of a Gothic cathedral. The similarity is not mere coincidence; whether in bone or other building materials, such structures provide the greatest strength with the least amount of weight.

4. The leg bones of *Apatosaurus* and its kin are stout, straight, and broad-ended. This enabled the legs to support a huge, heavy body, but didn't permit much flexibility in the joints. A modest amble of two or three miles an hour (average human walking pace) was probably the top speed of a full-grown sauropod.

5. The arrangement of the major muscles can be guessed at from the shapes of the fossil bones (ridges, knobs, or broad dished surfaces were probable attachment points), and from a knowledge of the musculature of living animals.

6. "What color were dinosaurs?" is a common question. Unfortunately, there is no answer to it. Rare pieces of fossilized skin (such as this replica of a fragment from the quarry) show the skin's texture, but their color has been altered by the minerals that replaced the soft tissue. Thus, from children's coloring books to museum murals, dinosaur colors are the artist's choice. In the past. most artists stuck rather conservatively to green, brown, and gray (like the drab sauropod in the small painting below), but in recent years there has been a refreshing trend toward brighter hues. The color and pattern of this *Apatosaurus* painting were borrowed from a modern lizard. Like lizards or any other group of animals, dinosaurs probably showed a wide range of coloration.

6.

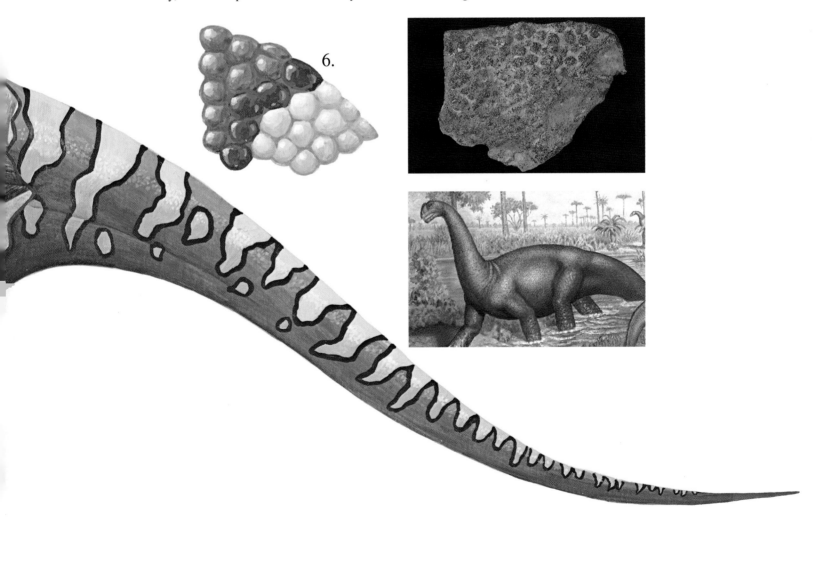

The Importance of Good Posture.

In the pages of this book we compare dinosaurs to elephants, giraffes, lions and other mammals. You may be wondering whatever became of the idea that dinosaurs were reptiles. Yes, they were reptiles on the basis of certain details of their skulls and other bones. But in another important respect they were quite different from the "saurians" for whom they are named.

Most living reptiles such as lizards and turtles have a sprawling posture, with their legs splayed out almost horizontally at the sides of their bodies. Crocodiles hold their limbs at an angle to the body but still have a fairly wide stance. In contrast, birds and mammals maintain an upright stance with the legs, more or less vertical and the feet directly under the body. Fossilized limb bones and trackways reveal that dinosaurs, whether two-legged or four-legged, did not sprawl in typical reptilian fashion, but stood straight-legged and upright.

What advantage does this posture offer? First, it requires less energy; second, it allows more rapid and agile movements. (Consider, in your own case, the difference between standing and squatting, or between running and doing push-ups.) Upright posture probably contributed a great deal to the dinosaur's success. While their relatives continued to shuffle along in the old reptilian pose, the early dinosaurs literally sprinted ahead of them into dominance of the Mesozoic world.

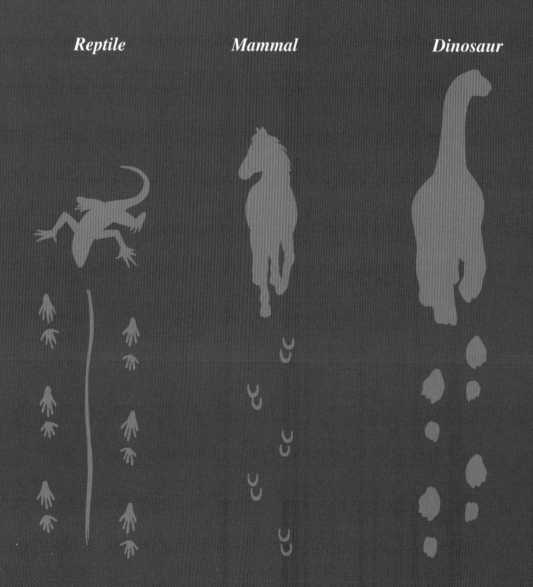

Reptile   **Mammal**   **Dinosaur**

A Lean and Mean Discovery

Dust whirls from a jackhammer's biting point and hand-held rock drills spit stone. In the background, generators yammer a relentless, lung-rattling drone. Wind whips sand into ears, up pant legs, down shirt collars, and seeps under goggles. Beneath the July sun, sweat plows down gritty backs and workers spit gnats inhaled on each breath. Reluctantly, an unknown dinosaur gradually emerges from an unexpected place.

As a helicopter lifts the packaged skeleton from its remote cliff, the crew knows they have unearthed an astounding dinosaur. *Allosaurus jimmadseni,* "AJ" for short, is not only a new species of rare theropod, or meat-eating dinosaur, it is also the most complete and articulated Jurassic theropod skeleton ever found anywhere.

It's taken four years to chisel this remarkable specimen from the fossilized river where it lay buried for 150,000,000 years. It will take another two in the laboratory to hew, cleave, needle and tweeze the skeleton from its rocky matrix. As preparers free individual bones, a better picture of the dinosaur emerges, and scientists delight in what they see.

Since researchers know most dinosaurs from a few bones or limited fragments, AJ is a paleontologist's dream: the skeleton is missing only a few ribs, mid-tail vertebrae, and its lower right leg. Its bones, aligned exactly as they would have been in life, give scientists a new view of allosaurs. "It appears," says Dan Chure,

A field worker wields a jackhammer to break up the stubborn, pebbly conglomerate encasing the new find.

the monument's paleontologist, "that AJ was a very slender, agile predator, not a barrel-chested, bone-crushing meat-eater like *Tyrannosaurus rex,* as we previously thought—which makes no difference if it's after you. But the disparity is impressive enough that we'll rebuild allosaur skeletons already on display."

AJ first flagged down researchers by poking its left foot unexpectedly from the Morrison Formation's Salt Wash Member. Most Western U.S. quarries, including Dinosaur's Carnegie Quarry, burrow into the Morrison's Brushy Basin Member. Although the two rock layers coalesced under similar environmental conditions, the poorly understood Salt Wash Member accrued millions of years before the Brushy Basin. This makes AJ about five million years older than dinosaurs in the visitor center's quarry wall.

Dan Chure is as excited as a kid with a new bike, "AJ contains features rarely

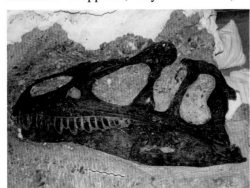

The unexpected narrowness of the new *Allosaurus's* skull suggests an animal well adapted to scavenging between the ribs of gargantuan sauropods. *Or not!* Trying to determine dinosaur behavior from the fossil record is an on-going challenge.

41

Explosives experts from Rocky Mountain National Park were called in to place charges in a ledge of rock above the quarry site.

seen in dinosaurs before," he beams, "and is vastly important for scientists studying carnivorous dinosaurs, especially *Allosaurus* anatomy and evolution. Since AJ is the most primitive allosaur known, it may unlock biological and evolutionary secrets."

This magnificent find does have one vexing problem: the skull is missing. It will be another two years before an elfish man appears from nowhere and finds the skull with a high-tech gadget fabricated from plastic pipe and electrical tape.

In the meantime, scientists measure, compare, and discuss this strange creature pulled with such effort from its sandstone bed. *Allosaurus jimmadseni* is, like all theropods, a bipedal carnivore. In a theropod line-up ranging from the 20-pound *Compsognathus* to the 45-foot-long *Tyrannosaurus rex,* allosaurs, at 30-feet long, would stand near *Tyrannosaurus.* Scientists estimate that AJ, who measures a mere 18.5 feet long, is a subadult not close to its maximum size. Allosaurs probably ate whatever they wanted and may have ambushed herbivores such as *Stegosaurus* or smaller predators like the 6-foot-long *Ornitholestes;* they could also have hunted in packs to bring down 70-foot-long sauropods like *Diplodocus.* The new view of thin-bodied allosaurs also means they would have made excellent scavengers, poking their narrow heads between giant sauropod ribs—or it could mean they fed in a way we haven't yet conceived.

Before AJ's discovery, paleontologists recognized only one allosaur, *Allosaurus fragilis.* Al, as he's known, is so abundant in Utah's Morrison Formation that he claims fame, like the rock star he is, as the official state fossil. Al and AJ differ in their vertebrae, pelvis, and skulls, but scientists may never know how different or similar they looked in life. Dan Chure asks, "Imagine you've never seen a peacock, and none are living. How would you ever determine, just by seeing its skeleton, what a peacock looked like?"

the sound of moving water. *Pterodactyls* squawk and jab at each other atop an allosaur carcass rocking in the current. They poke and pick at the dinosaur's eyes and nostrils while fish nip its leathery hide. Low and far-off, a sound gathers; ears prick, wings rustle, noses twitch. Rat-like mammals leap from hiding places within the carcass as their meal wavers in a gathering flood. The allosaur, its long tail pulled and tugged by

The resulting blast removed just enough rock from above the block containing the skeleton to make its removal much easier.

the surging current, bobs, then floats downstream. Deposited in a riverbend, the dinosaur disappears under tons of sand.

For millions of years, AJ's skeleton quietly meditates in its sandstone tomb. The earth turns in space; continents drift, mountains rise, and erosion digs ever deeper until the once-flat streambed stands encased in a sandstone cliff at the head of a narrow box canyon. To reach the site, workers walk one foot in front of the other like teetering high-wire artists, carrying generators, jackhammers, bags of plaster, sledges, and plenty of water. As the first hammer blow falls, one of the most complex excavations ever attempted at Dinosaur National Monument begins.

AJ, standing on the tip of its headless neck, leans into the cliff, and paleontologists spend two years chiseling until the skeleton lies mostly exposed and the rock above juts like a porch roof without supports. As excavators wrap the skeleton in plaster-soaked burlap, and shield it with sandbags, Dan Chure calls in a team of precision blasters from Rocky Mountain National Park. These "artists in dynamite" set their charges and neatly blast 300 tons of rock away from fragile skeleton. "Then," says Scott Madsen, a lead excavator, "the rock falls right back down so someone has to remove it." After four years, the excavators look like bodybuilders and the skeleton is winging its way to the monument's lab.

Still, Chure has no idea what happened to AJ's skull—it could have washed away soon after the dinosaur's death—but he suspects that because AJ is so complete, the skull must be nearby. Paleontologists probe and chip at AJ's quarry for weeks, but find nothing.

After the numbing drone of generators used outside it's comforting to hear the wispy humming of a pen-sized pneumatic scribe in the laboratory. Rock clings to the fossils like plaque on unbrushed teeth as Scott Madsen, staring into his microscope, gently cleans the skeleton's exposed bones. When finished, a life-sized latex mold will be poured to record the skeleton's exact position and articulations as it lay in the rock. One cast will be part of a new exhibit in the Quarry Visitor Center, and a copy will travel to other institutions. Next, Madsen carefully removes each bone for study, scientific description, and safekeeping. Dan Chure will spend three years studying AJ's bone structure and form to determine that AJ is unlike any known dinosaur.

After all this time, when Chure's hope of finding AJ's head has ebbed, Ramal (Ray) Jones calls to say he thinks he can find the missing skull. Dinosaurs fascinate Jones, a radiologist at the University of Utah's Radiological Health Department, and he tells Chure of his invention—the "dinosaur dowser"—a shielded gamma scintillation detector that measures radiation emitted by fossilized bone. Intrigued, Chure invites him to visit.

The rugged terrain of the quarry site dictated that helicopters would be necessarry to remove the 6,700-pound block containing the priceless skeleton.

The block was flown to the Quarry Visitor Center...

...where fossil preparators began the careful process of revealing the individual bones.

The exquisite preservation of AJ's skeleton is revealed by the presence of rare bones called "gastralia" which embraced the belly of the beast and supported a musculature which aided the dinosaur's breathing.

Scientists have long known that bones become radioactive during fossilization. Jones' dowser reads high gamma emissions (similar to light or x-rays) leaking from rock. After surveying AJ's excavation site, Jones discovers a hot spot on the cliff—but is this reading from a fragment of bone, a piece of petrified wood, or can it be the long-lost skull? As Chure crouches before the stony wall, Jones whispers, "Be careful; whatever it is, it's right below the surface." Chure swings his hammer and immediately hits bone, "within an hour," he recalls ecstatically, "it was clear we were looking at the back of the formerly missing skull."

As quarry preparators Ann Elder and Scott Madsen work to remove the fossil, they realize the ancient flood had pushed the skull about six feet downstream from AJ's neck. Although the right side is missing, the entire left side–braincase, jaw and teeth–remain preserved as one remarkable unit. Defying all the king's horses and all the king's men, AJ has been put back together again.

It has been 65 million years since a dinosaur last bent to drink from a quenching stream. Scientists look for the trigger, but they already know the reason dinosaurs went extinct: all species die out when their environment changes to the point it can no longer support them. Modern animals species from California condors to Utah prairie dogs now face that same possibility as human-caused environmental change transforms their habitat. But these animals are not alone. Just as in dinosaur times, the planet's dominant animal is as vulnerable as the meekest—for their habitat is our habitat.

Today, over AJ's quarry, winter clouds roll, but no rain falls. In the mountains, mule deer step easily through thin snow. The dry years mount. As hurricanes grow yearly stronger and tornadoes increase their devastation, as floods widen and droughts deepen, we look skyward and wonder.

Technicians prepare a latex rubber mold of the fully revealed skeleton. The resulting cast will be the centerpiece of a dramatic new Quarry Visitor Center exhibit.

The Long Sleep of a Tiny Dinosaur

Adult *Camptosaurus* could reach 18-feet in length and weigh 2000 pounds.

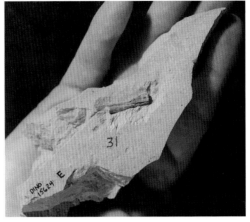

The tibia and fibula (lower rear leg bones) of the embryonic *Camptosaurus* are exposed in a fragment of fine matrix.

The rains have begun. Everywhere, sandy hills turn green as water seeps through mats of parchment-dry ferns. A meager creek swells.

Across this stream, a group of camptosaurs tend their mewling hatchlings. One adult female stands upright. At her feet, a leafy nest cushions four thick-shelled eggs. Eighteen-feet long and weighing 2,000 pounds, she scratches with her hoof-like claws at a beetle scaling her stout neck. An egg rocks and wriggles as the embryo within struggles for release. Dropping to all four feet the camptosaur nuzzles it back in place.

Abruptly, she stands upright again and sniffs deeply of the breeze. Dragonflies flick by on papery wings trailing the dusky smell of roiling water. The camptosaur herd bellows with alarm and moves off as the nests are quickly inundated. One egg cracks against a rock and discharges it's pint-sized cargo. The struggling embryo, freed at last, is gently buried in the mud and sand.

One hundred and forty-seven million years later—in 1991 to be exact—a tap from a tiny rock hammer releases the embryo into the palm of paleobotanist Dr. Sidney Ash. Smiling, he hands the find to Scott Madsen, a monument fossil preparator.

Back in the laboratory, Madsen peers into a binocular microscope and employs a sharp carbide needle to scrape individual sand grains from the embryo's 18-millimeter-long thighbone. He says, "This is a pretty nifty little find. Dinosaur embryos, hatchlings, and eggshells are rare in the Morrison. Although this is only a partial skeleton, it's the most complete embryo discovered in the formation, and the first ever of a camptosaur."

Every fossil specimen answers some questions and raises others. In this case, no eggshell was found near the skeleton leaving scientists initially pondering whether it was an embryo or a hatchling. As Scott's meticulous work further revealed the specimen's extreme small size, and the shape and structure of its bones, paleontologists concluded it was indeed an embryo. Until this discovery, most known Morrison hatchlings belonged to the dinosaur *Dryosaurus*. Embryonic dryosaurs have well-formed bones, indicating hatchlings were immediately able for fend for themselves. But camptosaur bones aren't fully hardened at hatching, implying that young camptosaurs were necessarily cared for by their parents and protected by the herd until they grew from bumbling nine-inch hatchlings into strapping four-foot juveniles.

One microscopic detail on the end of a tiny bone changes what's known about an entire species. Imagine the countless worlds swirling in the dust below our feet.

What's in a Name?

Most children love dinosaurs partly because the animal's names give them a chance to outdo their elders in the big words department. However, if you happen to be in the over-10 age bracket, don't despair—you too can speak *Dinosaurese*.

Dinosaurs lived all over the world, and so do the scientists who study them. To avoid having to translate names into dozens of different languages, scientists everywhere use Greek- or Latin-based names for dinosaurs just as they do for all plants and animals, living or extinct. Once you get to know the meanings of the root words, you'll find the names to be quite descriptive. Take, for example, the longest dinosaur name currently on record, *Micropachycephalosaurus*. Micro=small; pachy=thick; cephalo=head; saurus=lizard (or reptile). In other words, this was a small, thick-headed reptile. (Dinosaurs were not actually lizards but that translation is commonly used as well.)

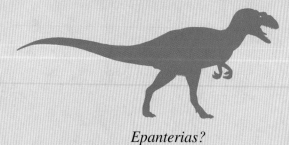

Epanterias?

The honor of inventing these tongue twisters goes to the first scientist who describes a new type of dinosaur in print, usually in a technical journal. Problems may arise, however, in defining just what a "new" dinosaur is. Suppose that you had found some fossils similar to the bones of an already named dinosaur, but just a bit different.. Was your specimen some other kind of animal or was it the same but just a bit younger? Or older? The opposite sex? Maybe it had arthritis?

If you were Othniel C. Marsh or Edward Drinker Cope, you would certainly have chosen the first case and created a new name. These two rival paleontologists were the driving force behind western America's "dinosaur rush" of the late 19th century, and they constantly strove to be the first to describe new dinosaurs from the steady stream of fossils shipped to them by their field collectors. Marsh ultimately named almost three times as many dinosaurs as did Cope, but he also duplicated himself more, assigning multiple names to similar fossils from different sites. For example, he named one set of bones *Apatosaurus* ("deceptive lizard," for its almost unbelievable size) and another set *Brontosaurus* ("thunder lizard," for its earth-shaking weight). A later scientist compared both groups of fossils and concluded that both represented the same type of animal. In such cases scientists prefer to retain whatever name was given first, and

Hypsirophus?

Claorhynchus?

because March used *Apatosaurus* two years earlier, it is technically correct, though *Brontosaurus* was better known to the public.

Finally, if you'd like to impress some youngster by rattling off a few dinosaur names that he or she has never heard of, try *Epanterias, Hypsirophus,* and *Claorhynchus*—some of Cope's inventions that reached print too late to beat out Marsh's *Allosaurus, Stegosaurus,* and *Triceratops.*

The Best in the West— or Anywhere

hen Earl Douglass discovered the first bones at the quarry site, the word "dinosaur" ("terrible lizard") was just a few decades old. British scientist Richard Owen had coined the name in 1841 to describe the strange animals whose fragmentary remains were beginning to be unearthed by fossil collectors. More complete skeletons were not discovered until the 1870s, and even then such finds were rare. Thus, as Douglass began to uncover that first *Apatosaurus,* dinosaurs were still quite novel to science, and what was "known" about many of them was as much guesswork as fact. The Dinosaur National Monument quarry soon changed that.

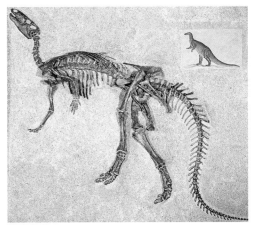

A few museums have more skeletons, but the Carnegie Museum probably has the nation's most impressive display of Jurassic dinosaurs— thanks to the Dinosaur National Monument quarry. Skeletons from the quarry dominate the Carnegie Dinosaur Hall. Shown here, from top to bottom, are *Stegosaurus, Camptosaurus, Apatosaurus,* a *Camarasaurus* juvenile, and *Dryosaurus.*

Although the quarry has produced no new species of dinosaurs, it has yielded a greater variety of species and a larger number of individual animals than any other single dinosaur site. Counting what was excavated and what remains in the rock, roughly 400 individuals, in varying

degrees of completeness and representing 11 different species, have been found.

However, the quarry's significance lies not just in the quantity but also in the quality of its fossils. Many of the quarry specimens are simply the best ever found anywhere. Eleven mounted skeletons from the quarry are on display in the Carnegie Museum and other museums across the country, and about a half-dozen more skeletons which are complete enough to be mountable are in museum study collections. Those on display range from the

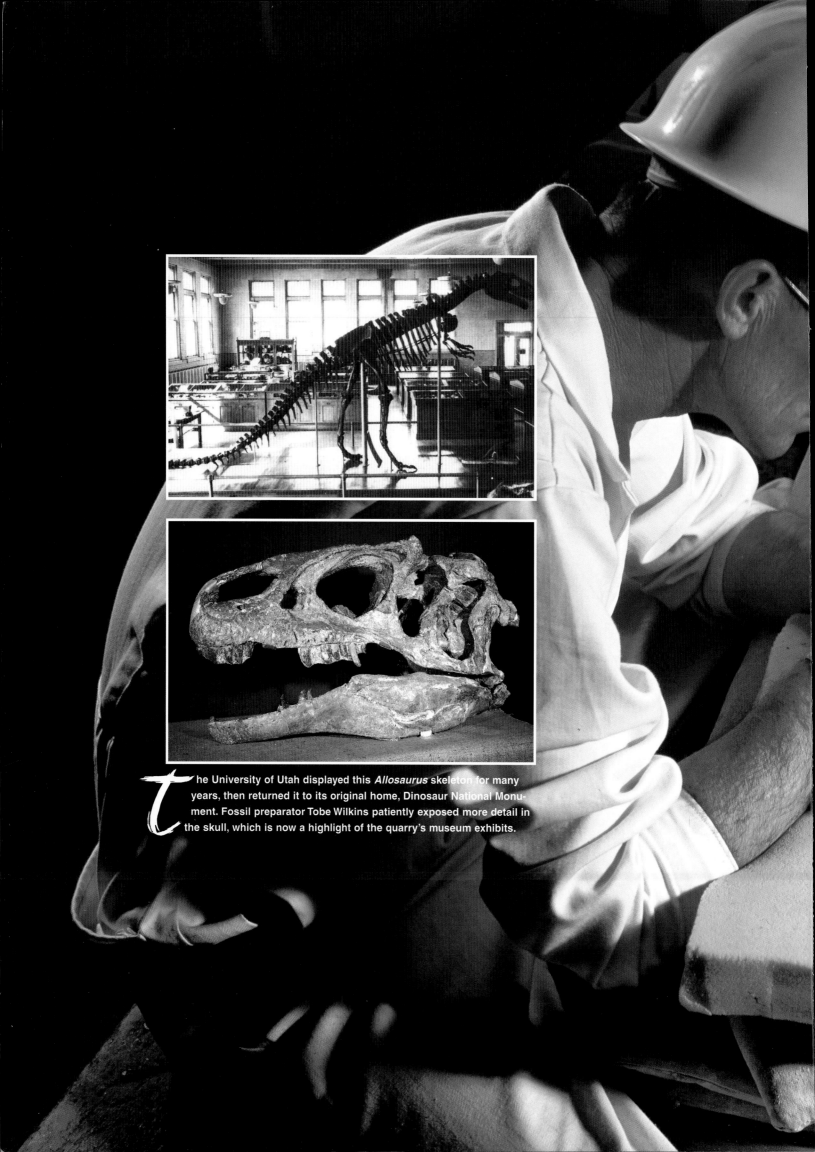

he University of Utah displayed this *Allosaurus* skeleton for many years, then returned it to its original home, Dinosaur National Monument. Fossil preparator Tobe Wilkins patiently exposed more detail in the skull, which is now a highlight of the quarry's museum exhibits.

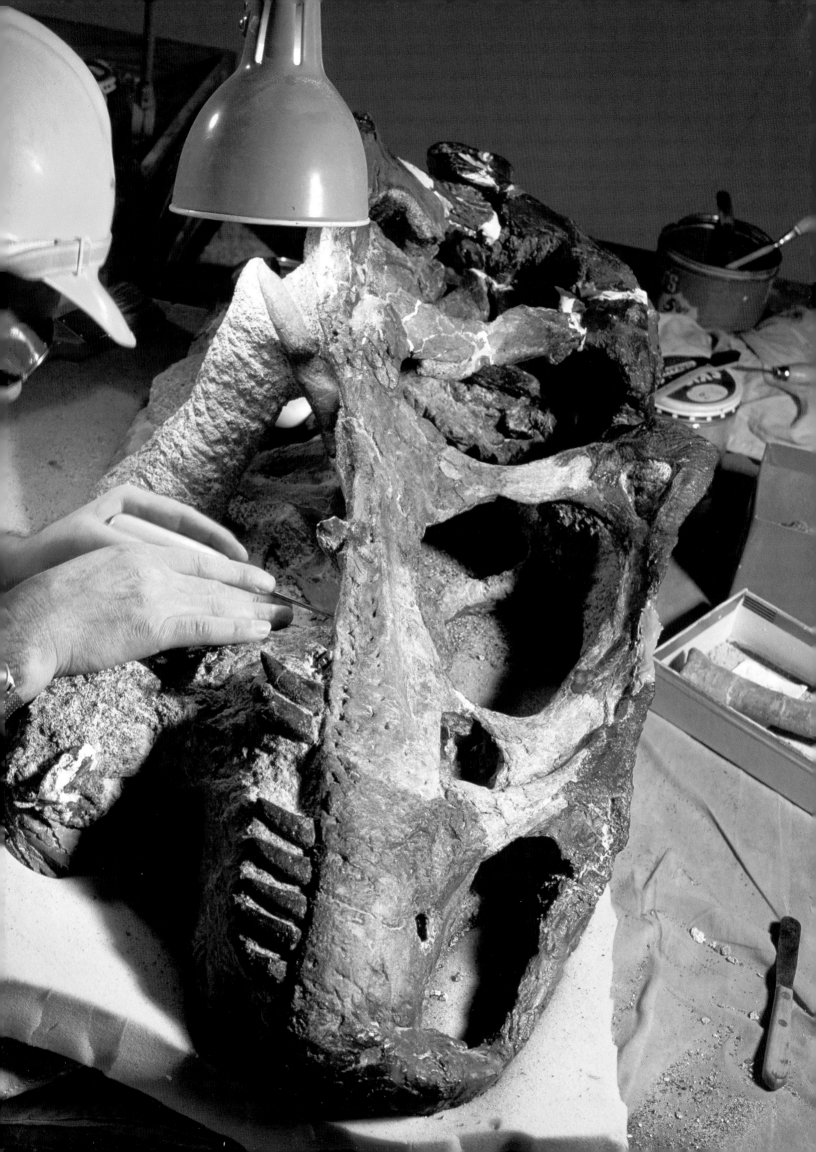

The Smithsonian Institution's efforts at the quarry netted it two fine display skeletons. One, a *Diplodocus,* stands in a conventional pose with its head towering over the other exhibits. the other, a young *Camarasaurus*, lies in the position in which it was found. From floor level it appears to be a shapeless heap, but a view from above reveals its completeness.

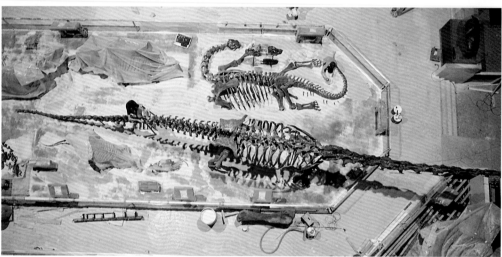

huge *Apatosaurus* to the diminutive *Dryosaurus.* Even three *Stegosaurus* skeletons could eventually be pieced together from the numerous fragments that had so annoyed Douglass. And there was one skeleton that did not even have to be put back together; this was the near-perfect *Camarasaurus lentus* mentioned earlier. Not only was it over 90% complete (in most cases, even 50% is cause for excitement), but almost all of the bones were still articulated in their correct positions. Douglass and his crew quarried it out in four large slabs, which the Carnegie Museum staff simply reassembled with the bones standing out from the rock like sculpture on an ancient temple.

That particular skeleton also represents another unique feature of the quarry—the large number of juvenile dinosaurs found in it. Because of their softer, underdeveloped bones, young animals are usually rare in the fossil record. That has not been the case at the quarry. In addition to the half-grown *Camarasaurus lentus,* juveniles of *Apatosaurus, Diplodocus, Dryosaurus,* and *Stegosaurus* (the partial

skeleton displayed in the Quarry Visitor Center) have been found. Even fossils of some junior turtles—fist-sized specimens of both *Dinochelys* and *Glyptops*—have been preserved.

Finally, most dinosaurs, from small to large, seem to have had an alarming tendency to lose their heads. Though their skulls were often sizeable, they were composed of many thin, fragile bones, and were only loosely attached to the necks. Thus, fossilized skulls are especially rare, and even when found they are often crushed or

Because of their rarity, dinosaur skulls are often reserved for special exhibits or studies, and cast replicas are placed on mounted skeletons, such as the Carnegie Museum's *Dryosaurus.* The original skull is the best specimen known for this dinosaur.

Diplodocus, whereas early paleontologists had assumed (relying more on the weighty opinion of Othniel C. Marsh than on any solid evidence) that *Apatosaurus* had a shorter, rounder head similar to that of *Camarasaurus.* Indeed, *Camarasaurus* skulls were often mounted on *Apatosaurus* skeletons for lack of anything better to put there. Finally, several leading scientists got together to review the situation, and they concluded that the skull Douglass had found probably does belong on *Apatosaurus.* Thus in 1979 the Carnegie

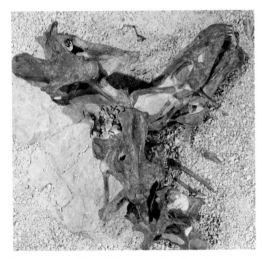

incomplete. The Dinosaur National Monument Quarry surpasses all others in this respect as well. Besides a good *Camarasaurus* skull still embedded in the quarry face, five others of that genus, two of *Diplodocus,* two of *Dryosaurus,* one of *Allosaurus,* and one of *Apatosaurus* have been excavated from the sandstone.

Many of these skulls are the finest specimens known, and the latter is the only one of its kind. Douglass found it just below the first *Apatosaurus* skeleton, but its identity was debated for many years. It is similar to the long, flat skull of

Museum ceremoniously beheaded the skeleton and replaced the old skull with the "new" one. Other museums have fol-lowed suit, using cast replicas of the Carnegie specimen.

The *Apatosaurus* head mystery could be solved once and for all if a skull could be found still attached to a recognizable *Apatosaurus* neck. Considering the record at Dinosaur National Monument so far, such a discovery may well lie in its future.

The continuing preservation of the quarry, and development of fossil sites elsewhere in the monument, will enable future generations of scientists and dinosaur enthusiasts to peer into the past, and perhaps to gain a new perspective on our own species' place in the long history of the Earth.

Photo Credits. Italics indicate page number and position.

Cover—McMullen & Milner Photography
Inside Cover—A. Hagood/NPS
Title Page—J.C. Benjamin/NPS

A Dinosaur Hunter's Dream
2; 11—A. Hagood/National Park Service
3—A.S. Coggeshall/courtesy of G.E. Douglass and Marriott Library, University of Utah
4, top and bottom; 6; 7, top and bottom; 8, all photos—Earl Douglass/courtesy G.E. Douglass and Marriott Library, University of Utah
5, all photos—Carnegie Museum of Natural History
9—Courtesy G.E. Douglass and Marriott Library, University of Utah
11, left inset—National Park Service
11, right inset—D. Matthews/NPS

Uncovering the Wall of Bones
12; 13, all photos; 16, left—A. Hagood/NPS
14, top and bottom; 15—T. Ricketts/NPS
16, center—J. Adams/National Park Service
16, right; 17, left—R. King/NPS
17, center—L. West/National Park Service
17, right—D. Davies/National Park Service

A World of Questions
19—Tom & Pat Leeson
20—C. McKnight/Dinosaur Nature Association
21, top—A. Elder/National Park Service
21, bottom—S. Madsen/National Park Service
22; 23—A. Hagood/National Park Service
25—S. Madsen/National Park Service

The Dinosaurs of Dinosaur
26—Illustration by J. Dawson
27, left; 30, top—L. West/NPS
27, right—L. Loetterle/NPS
28; 29—Carnegie Museum of Natural History
30, center, bottom right—T. Ricketts/NPS
30, bottom left—R. King/NPS

New Thunder on the Horizon
32; 34, bottom—A. Hagood/NPS
33; 34, top; 35—A. Elder/NPS
35—Illustration by J. Dawson

A Lean and Mean Discovery
41, top; 42; 44, all photos—A. Elder/NPS
41, bottom—D. Chure/NPS
43, top and middle—D. Papadokis/NPS
43, bottom—S. Madsen/NPS
45—Illustration by John Dawson
45—C. McKnight/Dinosaur Nature Association

The Best in the West—or Anywhere
47, all photos; 50, bottom; 51, middle, bottom—Carnegie Museum of Natural History
48; 49—A. Hagood/National Park Service
48, top inset—Courtesy Jim Madsen, Utah State Historical Society
48, bottom inset; 51, top—T. Ricketts/NPS
50, top, middle—Smithsonian Institution
52—J. Adams/National Park Service

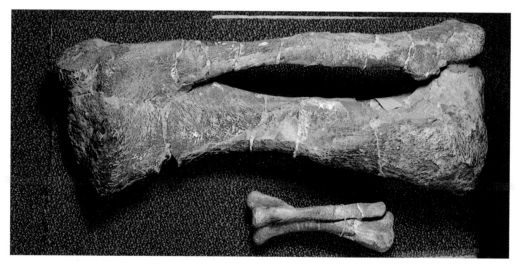

Juvenile dinosaurs—rare elsewhere—are a quarry specialty. These lower hind leg bones from the world's smallest *Stegosaurus* are about one-third the length of the same bones from an adult stegosaur.